To the Teacher

PURPOSE:

WORKING WITHIN WORDS helps pupils put sounds and other word elements to work to determine word meaning. Many units in WORKING WITHIN WORDS develop understandings about sound-symbol (phonic) associations. Other units treat letter combinations, syllabication, roots and affixes, accent patterns, compound words, longer words, and spelling changes caused by adding endings.

FOR WHOM:

The skill of WORKING WITHIN WORDS is developed through a series of books spanning ten levels (Picture, Preparatory, A, B, C, D, E, F, G, H). The Picture Level is for pupils who have not acquired a basic sight vocabulary. The Preparatory Level is for pupils who have a basic sight vocabulary but are not yet ready for the first-grade-level book. Books A through H are appropriate for pupils who can read on levels one through eight, respectively. **The use of the *Specific Skill Series Placement Test* is recommended to determine the appropriate level.**

THE NEW EDITION:

The fifth edition of the *Specific Skill Series* maintains the quality and focus that has distinguished this program for more than 25 years. A key element central to the program's success has been the unique nature of the reading selections. Nonfiction pieces about current topics have been designed to stimulate the interest of students, motivating them to use the comprehension strategies they have learned to further their reading. To keep this important aspect of the program intact, a percentage of the reading selections have been replaced in order to ensure the continued relevance of the subject material.

In addition, a significant percentage of the artwork in the program has been replaced to give the books a contemporary look. The cover photographs are designed to appeal to readers of all ages.

SESSIONS:

Short practice sessions are the most effective. It is desirable to have a practice session every day or every other day, using a few units each session.

SCORING:

Pupils should record their answers on the reproducible worksheets. The worksheets make scoring easier and provide uniform records of the pupils' work. Using worksheets also avoids consuming the exercise books.

To the Teacher

It is important for pupils to know how well they are doing. For this reason, units should be scored as soon as they have been completed. Then a discussion can be held in which pupils justify their choices. (The Integrated Language Activities, many of which are open-ended, do not lend themselves to an objective score; thus there are no answer keys for these pages.)

GENERAL INFORMATION ON *WORKING WITHIN WORDS*:

The units are of two types: concept builders and functional exercises. The concept units focus the reader's attention on common patterns and parts of words. Each generalization is built step-by-step on the structure of previously formed concepts. The functional exercises either follow the concept units or are contained within them. They provide the reader with many immediate and repeated experiences with words involving particular patterns or principles. Sentence settings are typical for the pupils' level; often the choices offered are new words.

As WORKING WITHIN WORDS progresses through different word elements there is constant reinforcement. The more elementary booklets focus on phonic elements such as consonant sounds, consonant substitutions, blends, phonograms, and vowel sounds. As the level of difficulty increases, the emphasis shifts to syllabication, prefixes, suffixes, and roots.

A unit-by-unit list of concepts developed in this book is found on page 64.

INSTRUCTIONS:

Minimal direction is required. Pupils' attention must be drawn to the answer choices. In the concept units only two or three answer choices are offered. In the units that provide application of understandings, four to nine answer choices are offered, providing more experiences with words of a particular pattern. In units which offer an *F* choice, the *F* stands for NONE. This means that none of the choices makes sense in that particular setting.

RELATED MATERIALS:

Specific Skill Series Placement Tests, which enable the teacher to place pupils at their appropriate levels in each skill, are available for the Elementary (Pre-1–6) and Midway (4–8) grade levels.

About This Book

As you learn to read, you learn the sounds that letters stand for in words. First, you look at the letters in a word. Next, you put together the sounds for the letters. Then you can tell what the word is.

Sometimes, two letters together stand for one sound. The letters *ch* stand for the sound you hear at the beginning of the word *chair* and at the end of the word *beach*. Some letters can stand for more than one sound. The letter *a* stands for the vowel sounds you hear in the middle of the words *hat* and *hate*. The sound for *a* in *hat* is called a **short *a*** sound. The sound for *a* in *hate* is called a **long *a*** sound.

You can think of a word as a kind of secret message written in code. You are trying to find the meaning of that secret message. You are trying to decode the word. The sounds the letters stand for are the key to unlocking the code.

Knowing the sounds of a word is only a beginning. Just as a secret message may have many parts, a word may have more than one part, too. In order to read and understand a word, you need to understand the parts of the word. For example, when you add *ed* to some words, it means that something is already done. It is the difference between *play* and *played*.

In this book, you will work with words in different ways. You will work with the sounds that letters stand for. You will work with word endings. You will see how two small words can make one big word. You will use different clues to unlock the meanings of words.

When you know the sounds that letters stand for, you will have one key to the code. When you know how word parts change the meaning of a word, you will have another key. You will be able to unlock the meaning of written words.

1. We saw a lion at the **z**_____ .

2. Mother said, "Do not play with **m**_____ ."

3. We saw a **p**_____ at the farm.

4. Dad wears a **v**_____ with his suit.

5. I can go up high with this **l**_____ .

6. The **f**_____ will make me feel cool.

7. Sam put his pet bird in a **c**_____ .

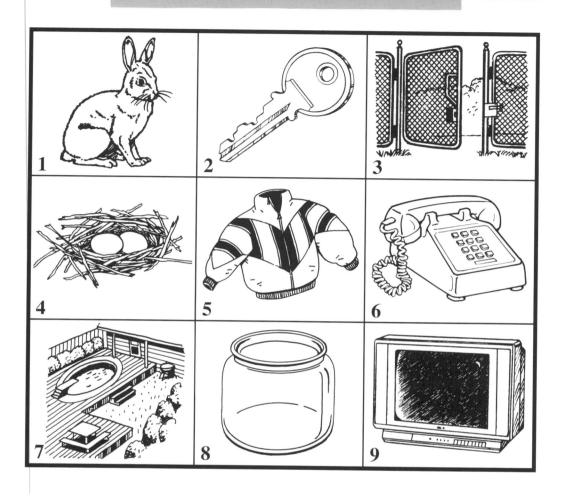

1. The **r**_____ ran into the woods.

2. I like to play in the **y**_____ .

3. When it gets cold I put on a **j**_____ .

4. Please don't forget to close the **g**_____ .

5. He liked to talk on the **t**_____ .

6. We will find the **k**_____ for the car.

7. Jan saw the **n**_____ up in the tree.

1. Please put the **s**_____ in the water.

2. Do you know who that **w**_____ is?

3. We saw a big **d**_____ running in the woods.

4. The **b**_____ flew into the sky.

5. The rooms in my **h**_____ are not very big.

6. What can I buy with this **qu**_____?

7. Betty has a big **b**_____ on her coat.

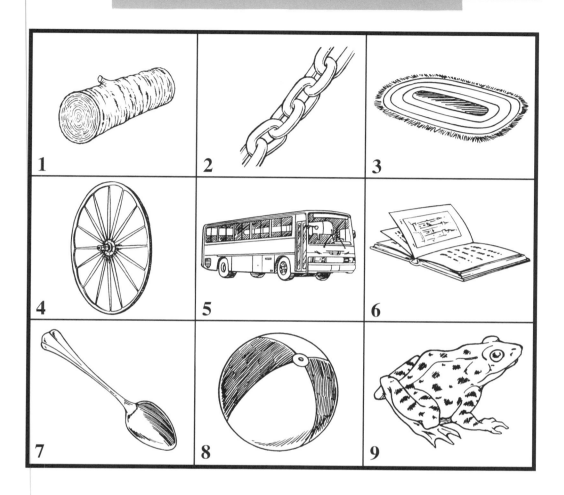

1. What _____**k** are you reading?

2. We saw the _____**s** stop at the store.

3. I will eat this with a _____**n**.

4. Ron saw a _____**g** jump into the water.

5. The baby likes to catch the _____**l**.

6. Where did you get that long piece of _____**n**?

7. They cut the _____**g** with a saw.

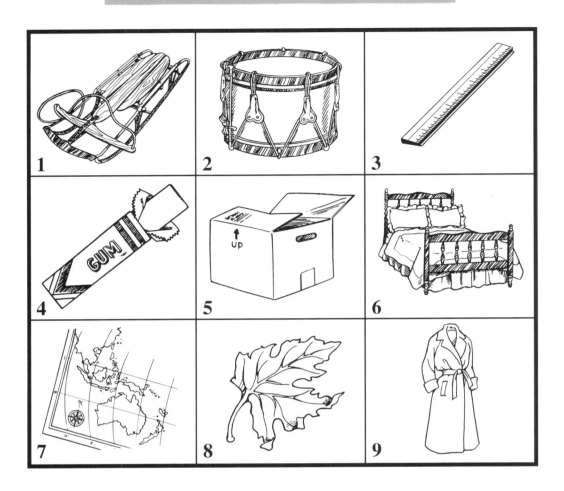

1. A _____**f** fell from the tree.

2. Ann let the boys ride on her _____**d**.

3. He said that Mother has a new _____**t**.

4. Jill took a book and _____**r** to school.

5. Put the toys in the _____**x**.

6. A _____**p** will help us find our way.

7. Sam asked Ben to get him some _____**m**.

1. Juan got a _____ from the store.

   (A) get   **(B) pet**   **(C) let**

2. Sam and Kim ran _____ Mike's house.

   (A) fast   **(B) last**   **(C) past**

3. Sandy will get in _____ of you.

   (A) back   **(B) pack**   **(C) tack**

4. Rick is not as _____ as Tom.

   (A) ball   **(B) wall**   **(C) tall**

5. How did you get _____?

   (A) net   **(B) bet**   **(C) wet**

6. You _____ and I will find you.

   (A) ride   **(B) side**   **(C) hide**

7. What _____ are you playing?

   (A) came   **(B) game**   **(C) same**

1. Ben is here, _____ Pam went out.

    (A) nut   **(B) cut**   **(C) but**

2. "They are not _____ here," said Jane.

    (A) in   **(B) win**   **(C) tin**

3. The boys had fun playing in the _____ .

    (A) and   **(B) hand**   **(C) sand**

4. "Mother will park the _____ ," said Sandy.

    (A) bar   **(B) far**   **(C) car**

5. "I think his name is _____ ," said Rosa.

    (A) boy   **(B) toy**   **(C) Roy**

6. Tom wants a _____ for his birthday.

    (A) funny   **(B) bunny**   **(C) sunny**

7. We must have _____ so we can see.

    (A) light   **(B) right**   **(C) fight**

UNIT 8
Consonant Substitution

1. Kelly will _____ a toy wagon for me.

   (A) make   (B) cake   (C) rake

2. Ann has a _____ in her backyard.

   (A) went   (B) sent   (C) tent

3. The boys put the cake into the _____ .

   (A) fan   (B) ran   (C) pan

4. A big _____ walked by me.

   (A) sat   (B) fat   (C) cat

5. The children had _____ playing in the water.

   (A) sun   (B) run   (C) fun

6. The little _____ ran down the road.

   (A) big   (B) pig   (C) dig

7. "I _____ help Father find him," said Meg.

   (A) will   (B) hill   (C) Bill

UNIT 9
Consonant Substitution

1. There are _____ people in our boat.

    (A) hen   **(B) ten**   **(C) men**

___

2. No one _____ out of my green wagon.

    (A) tell   **(B) bell**   **(C) fell**

___

3. There was a _____ hen on the farm.

    (A) bed   **(B) red**   **(C) fed**

___

4. Ron and I had a _____ this morning.

    (A) night   **(B) fight**   **(C) tight**

___

5. Jan _____ the big ball over the house.

    (A) hit   **(B) it**   **(C) sit**

___

6. "What did they _____?" asked his mother.

    (A) may   **(B) day**   **(C) say**

___

7. Mark _____ the children to the circus.

    (A) look   **(B) took**   **(C) book**

1. I know my sister was _____ there.

   (A) not   **(B) got**   **(C) pot**

2. Father asked Ann to _____ up the box.

   (A) Rick   **(B) sick**   **(C) pick**

3. My mother said, "Be _____ to animals."

   (A) find   **(B) kind**   **(C) mind**

4. The _____ ran after the two boys.

   (A) boat   **(B) coat**   **(C) goat**

5. Please tell us _____ to get there.

   (A) cow   **(B) how**   **(C) now**

6. We would _____ Sam to go with us.

   (A) like   **(B) bike**   **(C) Mike**

7. Bob got a big _____ when he fell.

   (A) hump   **(B) jump**   **(C) bump**

1. Mother will _____ us to the show.

    (A) take   (B) taking   (C) takes

2. Rosa was happy when she _____ the box.

    (A) opening   (B) opened   (C) open

3. Father will _____ us when to go to bed.

    (A) tell   (B) tells   (C) telling

4. Pam was _____ Tom make a big boat.

    (A) help   (B) helped   (C) helping

5. We are _____ a party for our friends.

    (A) give   (B) giving   (C) gives

6. Bob asked Ann to _____ at him.

    (A) looking   (B) look   (C) looked

7. Kelly is _____ to the store down the street.

    (A) walking   (B) walks   (C) walk

1. Andy is _____ a book about boats.

   (A) reads   **(B) read**   **(C) reading**

2. They saw a boy _____ in the yard.

   (A) plays   **(B) playing**   **(C) played**

3. Mother is out _____ in the boat.

   (A) fish   **(B) fishing**   **(C) fished**

4. Her sister will help us _____ the book.

   (A) finds   **(B) find**   **(C) finding**

5. He is _____ of going to the farm.

   (A) thinks   **(B) thinking**   **(C) think**

6. Maria _____ Juan to get her some milk.

   (A) asking   **(B) asked**   **(C) ask**

7. It is not good to _____ too fast.

   (A) eating   **(B) eats**   **(C) eat**

A. Exercising Your Skill

Read the sentences below. Pick the letter or letters from the box that goes in the blank.

1. I am a girl. My name is ____ill.

| B | J | W |

2. I am a boy. My name is ____an.

| St | Fr | N |

3. I live in the water. I am a fi____ .

| re | st | sh |

4. I fall in the winter. I am ____ow.

| cr | sn | kn |

5. I move along a track. I am a ____ain.

| pl | gr | tr |

Bill-Jill-Will-Phil

Can you think of a name that rhymes with yours? If you can, tell the class.

Silly Rhymes

Make up silly rhymes. Write a rhyming word for each animal's name. Choose words in the box.

1. ____ the cat   3. ____ the bug
2. ____ the pig   4. ____ the snake

| Jig | Tug | Bake | Flat |

B. Expanding Your Skill

Copy the word **N A M E S** across the top of your paper. Write any names you can think of that begin with each of the letters in the word *names*.

After you finish writing, you and your classmates read your lists. Cross out any names that someone else has written. The student with the most names left wins the game.

C. Exploring Language

Draw a line down the middle of a sheet of paper. Write these words at the top:

Today	Yesterday

Read the sentences below. Then write each sentence under the words **Today** and **Yesterday** on your paper. Change the action word in each sentence. One is done for you.

Sentences	Today	Yesterday
Rosa **is walking**.	Today Rosa **walks**.	Yesterday Rosa **walked**.
Ted is looking.		
Wilfred is acting.		
Kim is playing.		
Jerry is asking.		

D. Expressing Yourself

Do one of these things.

1. Write your name across the top of a sheet of paper. See how many words you can make from the letters of your name. Write the words.

   For example: Mary Beth Smith

may	be
the	it
ram	hit

2. Work with a friend. Make up some tongue twisters. Make most of the words in your tongue twisters begin with the same letter. Begin each twister with a name.

   Here is an example: Liz likes little lambs.

1. A little **b**_____ ran down the street.

    (A) ed   **(B)** oy   **(C)** ut

2. Tom lived **f**_____ away from the farm.

    (A) un   **(B)** ind   **(C)** ar

3. The girls came from the **s**_____ school.

    (A) at   **(B)** ame   **(C)** ight

4. I do not know just where to **l**_____.

    (A) ook   **(B)** ight   **(C)** et

5. It is a very **h**_____ day.

    (A) en   **(B)** ot   **(C)** ay

6. My father will not **l**_____ me go.

    (A) et   **(B)** ump   **(C)** ight

7. My new coat and hat are **r**_____.

    (A) un   **(B)** ake   **(C)** ed

1. That **m**_____ lives on my street.

   (A) ay   **(B) an**   **(C) ind**

2. Where did Sam put his new **h**_____?

   (A) ump   **(B) im**   **(C) at**

3. Jack got **h**_____ with the ball.

   (A) and   **(B) all**   **(C) it**

4. Kim took the **b**_____ out of the water.

   (A) oat   **(B) ig**   **(C) ent**

5. "He does not feel very **w**_____," said Mary.

   (A) ell   **(B) ide**   **(C) in**

6. Pete got **s**_____ from the boat ride.

   (A) ay   **(B) ell**   **(C) ick**

7. **B**_____ will let you have the bike.

   (A) ill   **(B) ack**   **(C) et**

UNIT 15
Blends: sl, pl, gl

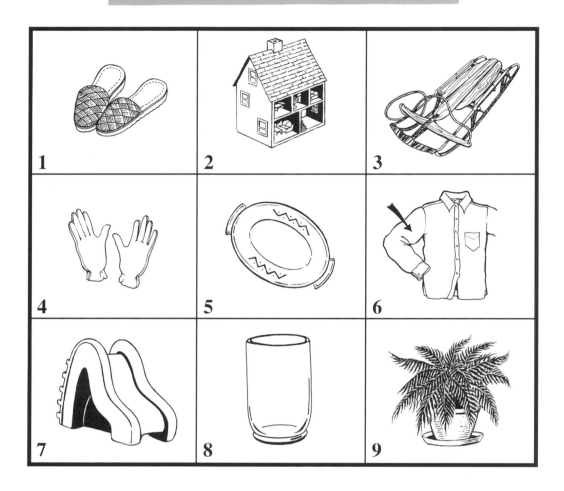

1. Ann went down the hill on my **sl**_____ .

2. What happened to the **sl**_____ of your coat?

3. Jenny wants to put on her new **gl**_____ .

4. Did you water the new **pl**_____?

5. Tom asked for a **gl**_____ of cold water.

6. There was no food on the **pl**_____ .

7. Mother put her feet into her **sl**_____ .

1. The **cl**_____ will tell you the time.

2. With a **fl**_____ we can see at night.

3. I saw a funny **cl**_____ at the circus.

4. What did he write on the **bl**_____?

5. Do you see the **fl**_____ at the top of the pole?

6. Peg has pretty **fl**_____ in her yard.

7. The baby likes to play with these **bl**_____ .

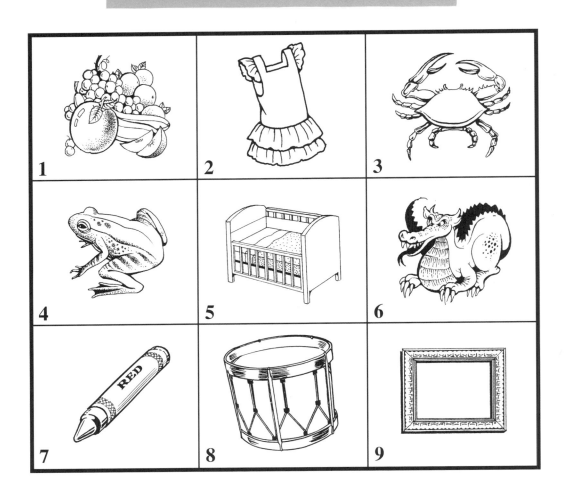

1. Would you like to beat the **dr**_____?

2. How many **cr**_____ are in that box?

3. Look out! There's a big **cr**_____ .

4. It is good to eat **fr**_____ every day.

5. Jane's friend gave her a pretty **dr**_____ .

6. The **fr**_____ jumped into the water.

7. The little baby can sleep in the **cr**_____ .

1. Are we going to cross the **br**_____?

2. The girls were playing up in the **tr**_____ .

3. Mother got some **br**_____ from the store.

4. A big **tr**_____ passed us on the road.

5. After school we had **gr**_____ to eat.

6. The **gr**_____ jumped onto the leaves.

7. Father brought the food to us on a **tr**_____ .

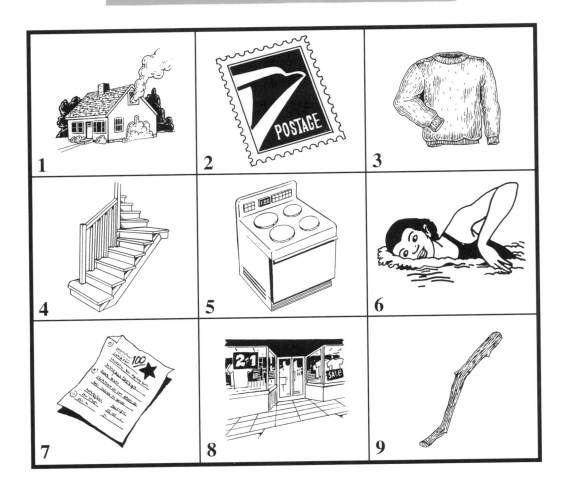

1. Rosa went to the **st**_____ for some milk.

2. The teacher put a **st**_____ on my paper.

3. The woman saw **sm**_____ coming from the house.

4. Her **sw**_____ will keep her warm.

5. Be careful walking down the **st**_____.

6. We will use that long **st**_____ as a pole.

7. Mother will show us how to **sw**_____.

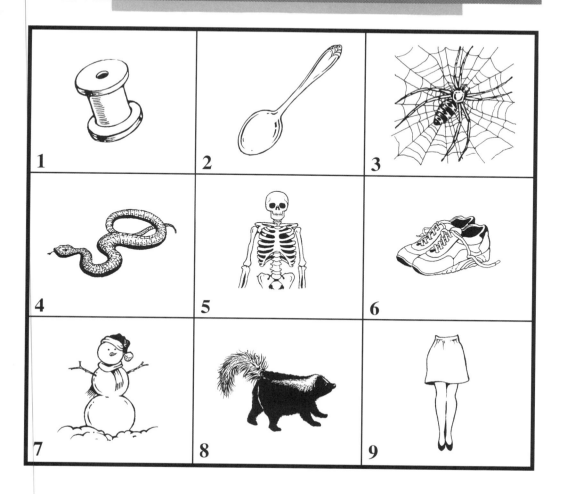

1. The children made a **sn**_____ in the yard.

2. A big **sp**_____ came down from a web.

3. You can see all the bones on a **sk**_____ .

4. I think I smell a **sk**_____ in the woods.

5. Rosa will wear a **sk**_____ and a jacket.

6. I wear my **sn**_____ when I play.

7. The baby likes to eat with the **sp**_____ .

1. Please sit down on the new **ch**_____ .

2. The **ch**_____ had fun at the party.

3. There is a **ch**_____ on top of that house.

4. I saw a big **sh**_____ far out on the water.

5. How many **sh**_____ do they have on that farm?

6. Sam put on the new **sh**_____ he got at the store.

7. The **ch**_____ wanted something to eat.

28

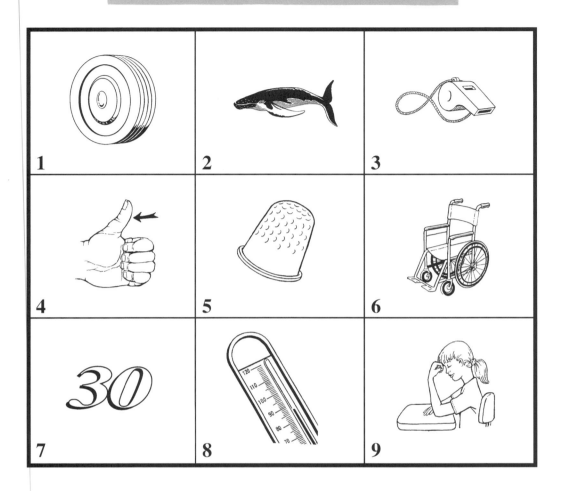

1. The wagon must have a new **wh**_____.

2. There are **th**_____ girls working over there.

3. She has a small cut on her **th**_____.

4. The **th**_____ shows how cold it is.

5. We could hear the **wh**_____ from far away.

6. She tried to **th**_____ of the answer.

7. We saw a **wh**_____ in the water.

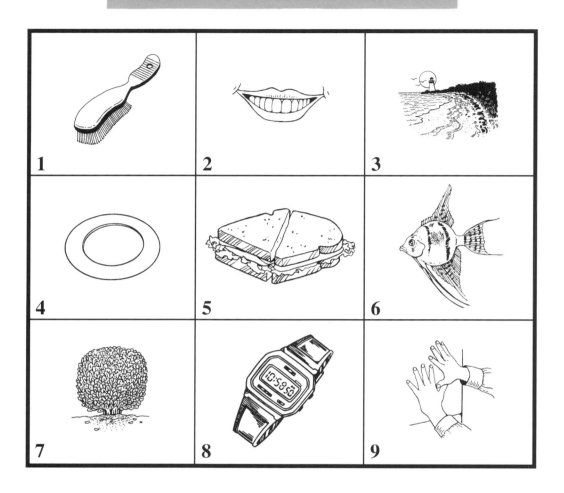

1. What meat is on my _____ch?

2. Rosa and Mary have pretty white _____th.

3. I use my _____ch to tell the time.

4. I played in the sand on the _____ch.

5. There is no food on the _____sh.

6. I see some _____sh in the water.

7. The bird has a nest in the _____sh.

1. I use the _____ to tell the time.

   (A) clock   **(B) block**   **(C) flock**

2. Last night Maria had a funny _____ .

   (A) cream   **(B) dream**   **(C) steam**

3. Ron brought the cake in on a _____ .

   (A) play   **(B) tray**   **(C) stay**

4. We saw a big _____ in the water.

   (A) ship   **(B) slip**   **(C) skip**

5. Jenny _____ a picture of the farm.

   (A) drew   **(B) grew**   **(C) chew**

6. The girls put the boats in the _____ .

   (A) shook   **(B) brook**   **(C) crook**

7. We went for a ride on a _____ .

   (A) train   **(B) chain**   **(C) stain**

A. Exercising Your Skill

Finish each poem. Add the letter in the circle to each word with a line under it.

(g)

Jane just <u>loves</u>
her new _____ .

(p)

Come here <u>soon</u>
and eat soup with a _____ .

(h)

Talk to a <u>cat</u>,
have a good _____ .

(r)

Don't step on a <u>tack</u>
as you run around the _____ .

(b)

Please sweep the <u>room</u>
with this _____ .

(s)

I'd run a <u>mile</u>
to make you _____ .

Make new words. Add one letter to change the beginning sound of each word below. Write the new words.

1. say   3. fog   5. lay
2. weep   4. back   6. rink

B. Expanding Your Skill

Read these word pairs. Make up a two-line poem using one of the pairs. Tell your poem to the class.

sing-sting   pay-play   wig-twig   loud-cloud

C. Exploring Language

Can you finish this poem? Pick a word from the box to rhyme with each underlined word. Write the poem. Correct all the mistakes.

Today I had very good <u>luck</u>.
I met a dragon. He's called _____ .
He's the prettiest thing I've ever <u>seen</u>,
Purple, silver, red, and _____ .
We used the fire from his <u>nose</u>
To make some toast and dry wet _____ .
We tied a kite to his long <u>tail</u>
And went out on the sea to _____ .

clothes	green	sail	Chuck

D. Expressing Yourself

Do one of these things.

1. Draw a picture of one of your favorite poems or nursery rhymes. Then ask your classmates to guess the poem. If you know the poem by heart, say the poem to your class.

2. Play a game of Rhymes and Riddles. Think of two words that rhyme. Make up a riddle. In the riddle, tell what word the answer rhymes with and give one other clue. See if a classmate can guess the answer.

Here are three examples:

I rhyme with **log**. I live in a swamp. (**frog**)
I rhyme with **more**. You buy things here. (**store**)
I rhyme with **room** and I sweep it clean. (**broom**)

1. Please push me high on this _____.

   (A) wing   **(B) swing**   **(C) sting**

---

2. The three girls were in _____ four.

   (A) grade   **(B) shade**   **(C) trade**

---

3. He has a _____ who looks just like him.

   (A) twin   **(B) chin**   **(C) skin**

---

4. They saw the _____ fly over the house.

   (A) blow   **(B) crow**   **(C) flow**

---

5. You will _____ your milk if you're not careful.

   (A) spill   **(B) drill**   **(C) still**

---

6. You didn't see a long _____ in our yard.

   (A) shake   **(B) flake**   **(C) snake**

---

7. How many words do you know how to _____?

   (A) spell   **(B) shell**   **(C) swell**

1. It takes work to _____ down a tree.

    (A) shop   **(B) drop**   **(C) chop**

2. The chair was a pretty _____ color.

    (A) gray   **(B) stay**   **(C) pray**

3. The circus pony did a _____ for us.

    (A) trick   **(B) stick**   **(C) brick**

4. Mother went to buy a _____ for a picture.

    (A) flame   **(B) frame**   **(C) blame**

5. That boy said his name is _____.

    (A) Fred   **(B) shed**   **(C) sped**

6. I saw the train coming down the _____.

    (A) black   **(B) crack**   **(C) track**

7. Will you _____ your friend with you?

    (A) bring   **(B) sting**   **(C) thing**

1. Look out or you will **dr**_____ it.

   (A) op   **(B) ew**   **(C) ess**

___

2. The ball hit Sam on his **ch**_____ .

   (A) op   **(B) ick**   **(C) in**

___

3. "The tree **gr**_____ so fast," said the woman.

   (A) ay   **(B) ab**   **(C) ew**

___

4. We can **tr**_____ the boat for the car.

   (A) ade   **(B) ick**   **(C) ip**

___

5. The boys played in the little red **sh**_____ .

   (A) ook   **(B) ot**   **(C) ed**

___

6. The children live in a **br**_____ house.

   (A) ake   **(B) oom**   **(C) ick**

___

7. There is a big **cr**_____ in the dish.

   (A) eep   **(B) ack**   **(C) eam**

1. Down came one big **fl**_____ of white snow.

   (A) **ake**   (B) **ame**   (C) **ag**

---

2. Please **br**_____ the chair to the girl.

   (A) **ing**   (B) **ake**   (C) **ick**

---

3. "I cannot find my **bl**_____ hat," said Ted.

   (A) **ess**   (B) **ame**   (C) **ack**

---

4. Look out or you will **sp**_____ the milk!

   (A) **ark**   (B) **oon**   (C) **ill**

---

5. "You can **st**_____ here with us," said Father.

   (A) **ay**   (B) **ar**   (C) **ing**

---

6. The car began to **sl**_____ down by the house.

   (A) **ed**   (B) **eep**   (C) **ow**

---

7. It is a **sh**_____ you will not see him.

   (A) **ame**   (B) **ell**   (C) **ade**

1. They live on our **bl**_____ .

   (A) ame   **(B) ew**   **(C) ock**

---

2. Is that a **cr**_____ in the water?

   (A) ack   **(B) ab**   **(C) ook**

---

3. Sam gave the **sh**_____ to his friend.

   (A) ame   **(B) ook**   **(C) ell**

---

4. "The **cr**_____ tastes good," he said.

   (A) ib   **(B) ash**   **(C) eam**

---

5. Mother got a new **bl**_____ car.

   (A) ack   **(B) ess**   **(C) eed**

---

6. A **sn**_____ is a very slow animal.

   (A) ow   **(B) ap**   **(C) ail**

---

7. I **th**_____ I can do the job.

   (A) ink   **(B) ick**   **(C) in**

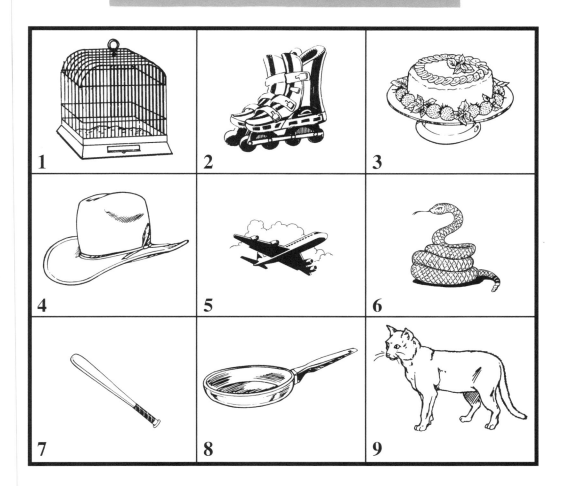

1. Father put on his new (**short a—**_____).

2. The bird flew out of its (**long a—**_____).

3. I will buy a pair of (**long a—**_____).

4. Ken asked Mother for a pet (**short a—**_____).

5. The food was cooked in a (**short a—**_____).

6. Try to hit the ball with the (**short a—**_____).

7. We will have some (**long a—**_____) to eat.

1. Do you know the _____ of that girl?

    (A) Jane   **(B) lake**   **(C) name**

---

2. I did not want to be _____ again.

    (A) cake   **(B) cave**   **(C) late**

---

3. I talked with a boy named _____ .

    (A) gave   **(B) Dave**   **(C) same**

---

4. Sam could not open the _____ .

    (A) gate   **(B) rake**   **(C) take**

---

5. It's not _____ to walk in the road.

    (A) came   **(B) Kate**   **(C) safe**

---

6. How I _____ to get up in the morning.

    (A) made   **(B) wave**   **(C) hate**

---

7. We can play a _____ in the yard.

    (A) bake   **(B) base**   **(C) game**

1. All of us are going on a _____ ride.

   (A) pail   (B) train   (C) rail

2. "Soon the heavy _____ will stop," said Jane.

   (A) jail   (B) rain   (C) wait

3. Do you think we will get some _____?

   (A) mail   (B) stair   (C) trail

4. Rosa and Kelly will _____ my wagon.

   (A) paint   (B) chair   (C) fail

5. We must have some _____ to go fishing.

   (A) bait   (B) pair   (C) chain

6. Mother put a big _____ on the boat.

   (A) sail   (B) pain   (C) hair

7. The boy's dog has a long _____ .

   (A) tail   (B) fair   (C) raid

1. Did you see which **w_____y** he went?

    (A) long a   **(B) short a**

---

2. How **h_____ppy** we were to see the show.

    (A) long a   **(B) short a**

---

3. Father put the toys in a big **b_____g**.

    (A) long a   **(B) short a**

---

4. Jan's pet **c_____t** ran away again.

    (A) long a   **(B) short a**

---

5. Juan opened the **g_____te** and ran out.

    (A) long a   **(B) short a**

---

6. Meg **s_____t** down under the apple tree.

    (A) long a   **(B) short a**

---

7. We saw a long train on the **tr_____ck**.

    (A) long a   **(B) short a**

1. We are going to eat a big (**long i—**_____).

2. He held the baby (**short i—**_____) in his hand.

3. It is fun to ride a (**long i—**_____).

4. (**short i—**_____) girls took a train ride.

5. (**long i—**_____) boys went to Ted's party.

6. That (**short i—**_____) is very fat.

7. Jenny likes to fly her (**long i—**_____).

1. It is _____ to go to the zoo.

    (A) mile   **(B) time**   **(C) ride**

_____

2. Mr. Well's _____ went with him.

    (A) hide   **(B) line**   **(C) wife**

_____

3. Ms. Carter helped us fly the _____.

    (A) kite   **(B) five**   **(C) pipe**

_____

4. The little dog didn't _____ me.

    (A) bite   **(B) fire**   **(C) mice**

_____

5. My father gave Ben a _____.

    (A) nine   **(B) side**   **(C) dime**

_____

6. Jill went for a long ride on her _____.

    (A) bike   **(B) dive**   **(C) five**

_____

7. Ms. Johnson's car needs a new _____.

    (A) pine   **(B) tire**   **(C) size**

1. Ann and I will catch some **f____sh**.

   (A) long i   **(B) short i**

---

2. Ted took a long ride on his **b____ke**.

   (A) long i   **(B) short i**

---

3. Mr. Green saw a **st____ck** in our yard.

   (A) long i   **(B) short i**

---

4. Yes, I think they are **h____s** books.

   (A) long i   **(B) short i**

---

5. They gave milk to the little **k____tten**.

   (A) long i   **(B) short i**

---

6. It is **n____ne** days before my birthday.

   (A) long i   **(B) short i**

---

7. There are **f____ve** children in the car.

   (A) long i   **(B) short i**

1. One cold day Kim made a _____.

   (A) homework   (B) snowman   (C) somehow

2. Maria saw a _____ up in our tree.

   (A) bedroom   (B) cannot   (C) bluebird

3. The baby played in the _____.

   (A) everyone   (B) almost   (C) sunshine

4. Bill and I like to play _____.

   (A) outdoors   (B) doorway   (C) without

5. Many children came into the _____.

   (A) schoolroom   (B) anyone   (C) maybe

6. The _____ came to put out the fire.

   (A) firefighters   (B) upstairs   (C) inside

7. The girls made a _____ in the yard.

   (A) playhouse   (B) daylight   (C) someone

Compound Words

1. The chickens were out in the _____ .

   (A) baseball   (B) postcard   (C) farmyard

2. _____ Ben is not on time for school.

   (A) Sometimes   (B) Daylight   (C) Railroad

3. Sam put on his _____ as he went out.

   (A) storeroom   (B) doghouse   (C) raincoat

4. "I will do it by _____," said Sue.

   (A) snowball   (B) myself   (C) herself

5. They were talking _____ our new school.

   (A) outside   (B) somewhere   (C) somewhat

6. Jill likes to play _____ with them.

   (A) basketball   (B) farmhouse   (C) backyard

7. Mother got Father a new green _____ to wear.

   (A) overcoat   (B) become   (C) doorbell

A. Exercising Your Skill

Read the questions and the words in each row. Listen to the sounds at the beginning of each word. Then write your answer.

1. Which one is up in the sky?   loud   cloud   proud
2. What can fall in winter?   snow   grow   blow
3. Which one can make you wet?   train   rain   brain
4. Which one can you sit on?   fair   pair   chair
5. What does wind do?   show   glow   blow

B. Expanding Your Skill

Here are some word riddles. Work with a partner to answer them. Write the letters that finish each word.

1. I am a cool place with no sun.
   I am sh_____ .

2. I keep the rain and cold out of your house.
   I am a window _____ne.

3. I am the name of a color.
   I am _____ow.

4. I am a time of the year.
   I am sp_____ .

5. I am one who teaches.
   I am a _____er.

C. Exploring Language

The underlined word in each sentence does not make sense. Change the *first* letter of the underlined word so that the word does make sense. Write the new words on your paper.

1. Rosa is happy when the <u>run</u> does not shine.
2. She loves to play in the <u>pain</u>.
3. Rosa has a <u>fig</u> umbrella.
4. It keeps her <u>fry</u>.
5. Rosa also wears <u>hoots</u> on her feet.
6. She does not get <u>bet</u> feet.
7. Rosa always has a good <u>dime</u> in the rain.

D. Expressing Yourself

Do one of these things:

1. Pretend that you work on the TV news. Make up a weather report. Tell what will happen today and tomorrow. Show the weather on the board. Give your weather report to the class.

2. What would happen if it rained orange juice, hailed apples, and snowed ice cream? Talk about it with a group. Think of other funny kinds of weather. After you talk, tell your group's ideas to the whole class.

3. Make lists of the kinds of clothes you wear in summer and in winter. Draw a picture of clothes for each time of year. Write a sentence or two to tell why you wear different clothes in summer and in winter.

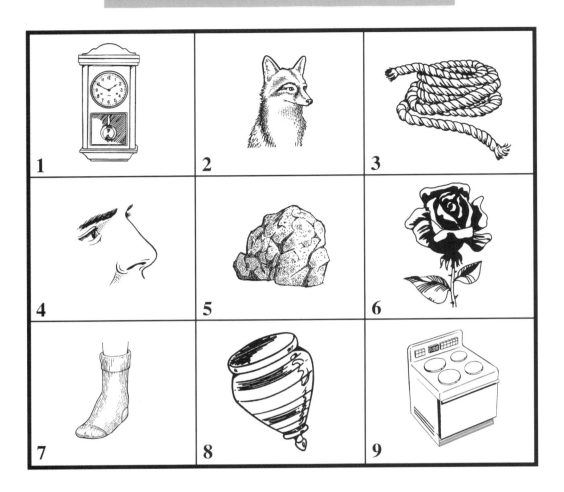

1. I picked a red (**long o—**_____) from the garden.

2. Ron will cook the food on the (**long o—**_____).

3. They could not move the huge (**short o—**_____).

4. A (**short o—**_____) is a very fast animal.

5. The children like to jump (**long o—**_____).

6. Ted put his (**short o—**_____) on his feet.

7. The girl played with the (**short o—**_____).

1. The children played a _____ on Bill.

   (A) joke   **(B) home**   **(C) note**

2. Lee saw a _____ in the boat.

   (A) nose   **(B) poke**   **(C) hole**

3. Sam saw a red _____ in our garden.

   (A) hope   **(B) rose**   **(C) stove**

4. I did not know _____ children.

   (A) pole   **(B) stone**   **(C) those**

5. They asked us to _____ for Sue.

   (A) rode   **(B) rope**   **(C) vote**

6. "Please _____ the door," said Father.

   (A) close   **(B) bone**   **(C) robe**

7. She _____ me to go with them.

   (A) hole   **(B) chose**   **(C) role**

1. Rosa gave her friend a toy **d____ll.**

   (A) long o   **(B) short o**

---

2. Many children like to jump **r____pe.**

   (A) long o   **(B) short o**

---

3. The baby played with his **bl____cks.**

   (A) long o   **(B) short o**

---

4. Ron asked to sleep on the new **c____t.**

   (A) long o   **(B) short o**

---

5. Mother put a **l____ck** on the back door.

   (A) long o   **(B) short o**

---

6. Ms. Carter did not take a **b____at** ride.

   (A) long o   **(B) short o**

---

7. The baby **f____x** looks like a dog.

   (A) long o   **(B) short o**

1. Grandmother saw the (**short e—**_____) in the tree.

2. (**long e—**_____) boys walked in the cold snow.

3. We will have (**long e—**_____) for dinner.

4. The wool comes from (**long e—**_____).

5. Would you like to eat an (**short e—**_____)?

6. There was just one (**long e—**_____) on the tree.

7. (**short e—**_____) chickens ran into the garden.

1. The boy's bedroom is very _____ .

    (A) leaf   **(B) heat**   **(C) neat**

2. There is an apple for _____ of us.

    (A) team   **(B) each**   **(C) reach**

3. Mother will _____ us how to do it.

    (A) meal   **(B) eat**   **(C) teach**

4. Jill was _____ to her little brother.

    (A) mean   **(B) tea**   **(C) beat**

5. What kind of _____ do you like to eat?

    (A) beast   **(B) cheap**   **(C) meat**

6. Kim did not _____ what Mother said.

    (A) hear   **(B) cheat**   **(C) please**

7. Father showed Bob how to _____ the room.

    (A) ear   **(B) deal**   **(C) clean**

1. I burned the _____ that I made for lunch.

   (A) toast   (B) goat   (C) boat

2. The puppy chased a _____ in the garden.

   (A) coal   (B) load   (C) toad

3. "Put on your new _____," said Father.

   (A) coat   (B) loaf   (C) coach

4. Ben will not _____ in his old bed.

   (A) meet   (B) sleep   (C) feet

5. I did not _____ very well this morning.

   (A) cheese   (B) sheep   (C) feel

6. Meg showed Ted how to brush his _____.

   (A) bee   (B) bleed   (C) teeth

7. The little squirrel ran down the _____.

   (A) sweep   (B) tree   (C) sweet

1. Grandmother gave us some **m____at** to eat.

   (A) long e   **(B) short e**

2. The bird made a **n____st** in the tree.

   (A) long e   **(B) short e**

3. We put up our **t____nt** in the yard.

   (A) long e   **(B) short e**

4. Juan went down the hill on the **sl____d**.

   (A) long e   **(B) short e**

5. Grandfather has a **d____sk** in his room.

   (A) long e   **(B) short e**

6. Father will buy Ann a new **dr____ss**.

   (A) long e   **(B) short e**

7. Jan put her **f____et** into the water.

   (A) long e   **(B) short e**

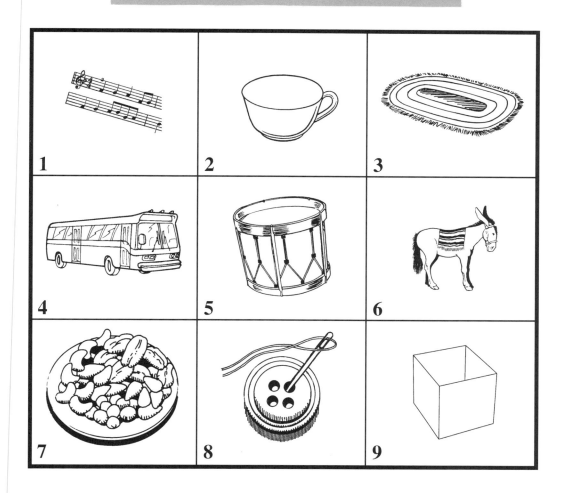

1. That animal is a (**long u**—_____).

2. Mother can sing and read (**long u**—_____).

3. Put some milk in the (**short u**—_____).

4. Do not walk on the new (**short u**—_____).

5. We would like some (**short u**—_____) to eat.

6. How many people can ride on the (**short u**—_____)?

7. The block is in the shape of a (**long u**—_____).

1. I think a **m____le** looks like a horse.

    (A) long u   **(B) short u**

---

2. The men put the box in the **tr____ck**.

    (A) long u   **(B) short u**

---

3. Ann knows how to play the **dr____m**.

    (A) long u   **(B) short u**

---

4. The **d____ck** jumped into the water.

    (A) long u   **(B) short u**

---

5. "I like to walk on the new **r____g**," she said.

    (A) long u   **(B) short u**

---

6. The baby was as **c____te** as it could be.

    (A) long u   **(B) short u**

---

7. Ted can read **m____sic** and sing well.

    (A) long u   **(B) short u**

1. The car ran out of **g**____**s**.

    (A) short a   **(B) short u**

---

2. We will clean the floor with this **m**____**p.**

    (A) short a   **(B) short o**

---

3. The box was made out of **t**____**n.**

    (A) short i   **(B) short e**

---

4. The baby sat on Father's **l**____**p.**

    (A) short i   **(B) short a**

---

5. Ben put the apples into the **p**____**n.**

    (A) short i   **(B) short a**

---

6. We took a long **tr**____**p** in the car.

    (A) short a   **(B) short i**

---

7. The little baby was in her **cr**____**b.**

    (A) short i   **(B) short a**

1. Ben will **h_____de,** and we will try to find him.

    (A) long u   **(B) long i**

---

2. Sam and I got a **r_____se** from my garden.

    (A) long i   **(B) long o**

---

3. The car went down the **r_____ad.**

    (A) long o   **(B) long e**

---

4. A **l_____af** fell from the tree.

    (A) long e   **(B) long o**

---

5. The three girls **l_____ke** to play games.

    (A) long i   **(B) long a**

---

6. The green apple is not **r_____pe** just now.

    (A) long o   **(B) long i**

---

7. We like to **r_____ad** many books.

    (A) long e   **(B) long o**

1. This bike is _____ than that one.

   (A) newer　　　　　　**(B) newest**

2. That is the _____ tree in the park.

   (A) biggest　　　　　　**(B) bigger**

3. Peg can run _____ than Ron can.

   (A) fastest　　　　　　**(B) faster**

4. She is the _____ girl in our room.

   (A) smartest　　　　　　**(B) smarter**

5. The little boy is _____ than his sister.

   (A) kinder　　　　　　**(B) kindest**

6. He is the _____ boy in the school.

   (A) funniest　　　　　　**(B) funnier**

7. Jenny looked _____ than her brother.

   (A) happiest　　　　　　**(B) happier**

A. Exercising Your Skill

Look at the boxes. Tell what *-er* and *-est* words are missing.

small smaller smallest	loud _____ loudest	tall _____ tallest	big bigger _____

hot hotter _____	old _____ oldest	light lighter _____	cold _____ coldest

Now pick one of the boxes. Name three things that tell about each of the three words in that box.

B. Expanding Your Skill

Play "-er, -est." Pick someone to be leader first. The leader thinks of something in the room. The rest of the class asks questions to try to guess what it is. All the questions must use **-er** or **-est**. Here are some things you could ask:

Is it higher than I can reach?
Is it bigger than a pencil?
Is it closer to me than to Wes?
Is it the biggest thing in the room?

The student who guesses the object is the new leader.

C. Exploring Language

Pat always likes to have a bigger, better idea than Matt. Write what Pat says. Fill in the blanks.

Matt	A flower is pretty.	A _____ is prettier.	Pat
Matt	A purple spider is strange.	A _____ is much stranger.	Pat
Matt	A bat is ugly.	A _____ is uglier.	Pat
Matt	A picnic is nice.	A _____ is nicer.	Pat

D. Expressing Yourself

Have an **-est** cont**est**. Write the thing you can think of that is:

biggest _____   smallest _____
hottest _____   prettiest _____
coldest _____   ugliest _____
farthest away _____

Compare your answers with the answers of four classmates. Vote on the best answer for each one.

CONCEPTS DEVELOPED

UNIT

1. INITIAL CONSONANTS: F, C, L, M, P, V, Z

2. INITIAL CONSONANTS: T, N, R, K, G, J, Y

3. INITIAL CONSONANTS: B, H, S, W, D, Q+U

4. FINAL CONSONANTS: G, L, S, K, N

5. FINAL CONSONANTS: T, F, M, R, P, D, X

6. CONSONANT SUBSTITUTION

7. CONSONANT SUBSTITUTION

8. CONSONANT SUBSTITUTION

9. CONSONANT SUBSTITUTION

10. CONSONANT SUBSTITUTION

11. WORD ENDINGS: S, ED, ING

12. WORD ENDINGS: S, ED, ING

13. CONSONANTS & PHONOGRAMS

14. CONSONANTS & PHONOGRAMS

15. CONSONANT BLENDS: SL, PL, GL

16. CONSONANT BLENDS: CL, FL, BL

17. CONSONANT BLENDS: CR, FR, DR

18. CONSONANT BLENDS: GR, BR, TR

19. CONSONANT BLENDS: ST, SW, SM

20. CONSONANT BLENDS: SP, SN, SK

21. INITIAL DIGRAPHS: SH, CH

22. INITIAL DIGRAPHS: TH, WH

23. FINAL DIGRAPHS: CH, SH, TH

24. BLEND & DIGRAPH SUBSTITUTION

25. BLEND & DIGRAPH SUBSTITUTION

UNIT

26. BLEND & DIGRAPH SUBSTITUTION

27. BLENDS, DIGRAPHS & PHONOGRAMS

28. BLENDS, DIGRAPHS & PHONOGRAMS

29. BLENDS, DIGRAPHS & PHONOGRAMS

30. VOWELS: LONG & SHORT A

31. MAGIC E WORDS: A PATTERN

32. DOUBLE VOWEL WORDS: AI PATTERN

33. VOWELS: LONG & SHORT A

34. VOWELS: LONG & SHORT I

35. MAGIC E WORDS: I PATTERN

36. VOWELS: LONG & SHORT I

37. COMPOUND WORDS

38. COMPOUND WORDS

39. VOWELS: LONG & SHORT O

40. MAGIC E WORDS: O PATTERN

41. VOWELS: LONG & SHORT O

42. VOWELS: LONG & SHORT E

43. DOUBLE VOWEL WORDS: EA

44. DOUBLE VOWEL WORDS: OA & EE

45. VOWELS: LONG & SHORT E

46. VOWELS: LONG & SHORT U

47. VOWELS: LONG & SHORT U

48. MIXED SHORT VOWELS

49. MIXED LONG VOWELS

50. ENDINGS: ER, EST

Book B

Specific Skill Series

Working Within Words

Richard A. Boning

Fifth Edition

SRA/McGraw-Hill
Columbus, Ohio